TO LIVE AT THE PITCH

by
Roger Karshner

FOUNDED 1830

New York Hollywood London Toronto

WWW.SAMUELFRENCH.COM

IMPORTANT BILLING AND CREDIT REQUIREMENTS

CHARACTERS

OPHELIA
MILO
ADAMDONG
DOCTOR
CALVIN
DIPLOMAT*
PASCAL
BILL
SAILOR*
MARINE*

* To be played by the same actor.

If I could only live at the pitch that is near madness
When everything is as it was in my childhood
Violent, vivid, and of infinite possibility:
That the sun and the moon broke over my head.

RICHARD EBERHART
"If I Could Only Live at the Pitch
that is Near Madness"

ACT I

Scene 1

(Set is an all-purpose room in an old Victorian mansion. It is filled with a hodgepodge of crap. The furniture is a strange mixture of ancient, old, modern and just plain junk. Paintings are of varied periods and styles. There is a large table filled with scientific stuff: test tubes, Bunsen burners, coils, motors, tools, wire, an operating table, etc. There is a large, dirty, dented refrigerator in one corner. A large chalk board. The walls are plastered with one-sheets from old horror movies. A swing is suspended from the ceiling. There is an archaic, beat-up dentist's chair and antique dental instruments. On the wall UP is a huge banner reading — "Stanley Hooker Institute Of Technology." There is an Exercycle with a basket and klaxon horn and red, white and blue crepe paper woven through its wheels. Papers and magazines are strewn all over the joint. The place is a downright mess.

There is a coat rack with a man hanging from it. He is a "ventriloquist's dummy" named MILO. MILO has wild orange hair and a brightly painted face: painted smile, eyes, a red nose. He is wearing a cutaway coat adorned with medals, a white winged-collar shirt with a black bow tie, and a pair of tattered blue jeans. There is wide red sash across his breast. He is bare-

7

foot and his toenails are painted alternately red, white and blue. There is a boxing glove on his left hand. Milo is usually motionless.

AT RISE the set is uninhabited. Then, OPHELIA RASS ENTERS. She's wearing orange pedal pushers, blown-out athletic shoes, the top portion of a baseball player's uniform. She's carrying a huge ball of yarn and knitting needles. She goes directly to a well-stocked bar, pours herself a stiff drink and belts it down like a sailor on leave.)

OPHELIA. *(Smacking her lips.)* Ah! Wonderful! Straight from the Great God Juiceifer. *(She sings as she crosses toward MILO. The melody is based on "I Want A Girl, Just Like the Girl Who Married Dear Old Dad.")*
I want a belt
Just like the belt
That loosened Daddy's fly....

(As OPHELIA passes MILO she unzips his fly precisely on the word "fly." Emotionless, mechanically, MILO zips himself up. OPHELIA goes to the Exercycle, tosses the yarn and needles into the basket, mounts the bike, honks the klaxon and begins to pedal like crazy. She takes up the needles and begins to knit.

ADAMDONG KLOSTERHAGEN ENTERS. He's wearing a mailman's uniform and spats. As he crosses to the refrigerator he pats MILO's head affectionately.)

ADAMDONG. Good morning, my dear Milo. *(Adamdong steps behind MILO and appears to manipulate him as a ventriloquist would, his mouth moving obviously.)* Good morning, Adamdong.

TO LIVE AT THE PITCH

How are you? *(As himself.)* Fine, Milo.

(ADAMDONG goes to the refrigerator, opens it. Blatantly observable inside are the carcasses of frozen animals — a rabbit, dog, cat, mouse, bird, hamster. He removes a stiff gray squirrel from his mailman's pouch and tosses it into the fridge. He roughly shoves aside animal remains, withdraws a half-gallon of milk, kicks the fridge door shut with his foot. He takes a dirty glass from the bar and pours himself a slug of milk, removes his mailman's cap and takes a plastic-wrapped sandwich from its crown. He casually tosses the cap to a corner, drapes his mail pouch over a chair, unwraps the sandwich and begins to munch.)

OPHELIA. *(Knitting and pumping.)* You appear to be weary, my dear Adamdong.

ADAMDONG. *(Through a gulp of milk.)* I have been on an extended trek today, Ophelia. I have trudged over the vast expanses of the county in search of perfect specimens. Through marsh land, over high tors, under bridges, and into the recesses of three drainage projects. I even resorted to descending into the sewers. I have poked and prodded among tons of rubbish: broken dolls, hat pins, jagged glass, old bottles, discarded candy wrappers. I even gutted an old mildewed Morris chair in my quest for creatures necessary to my experimentation.

OPHELIA. You are an exacting man, Adamdong Klosterhagen. Too a fault. You've got to stop making love with the aid of a slide rule.

ADAMDONG. One must take every precaution to avoid wasted motion.

OPHELIA. Your dedication to perfection is straining our relationship.

ADAMDONG. Such is science. What are you knitting, Ophelia

dear?

OPHELIA. A sweater for my pumpkin.

ADAMDONG. And how is Henrietta?

OPHELIA. Much to my distress, I found mice nibbling at her this morning.

ADAMDONG. Green or purple mice?

OPHELIA. Orange.

ADAMDONG. Orange? Most difficult to discern in a pumpkin patch.

OPHELIA. But never the less, beautiful little creatures.

ADAMDONG. Yes.

OPHELIA. Orange mice always bring to mind our initial contact.

ADAMDONG. They were there with us in the piano crate when I first tasted your delights.

OPHELIA. They squeaked throughout the entire incident.

ADAMDONG. And I, foolish one, thought it was the mattress.

OPHELIA. Well, I do believe there were several in the ticking.

ADAMDONG. Pushy little devils.

OPHELIA. I said farewell to my virginity on a bed of orange mice.

ADAMDONG. Virginity? Hardly. I'm afraid, Ophelia, that your virginity had flown many years before our initial contact.

OPHELIA. Yes, I must confess. At the age of thirteen, as a matter of fact, I was attacked by a strange looking sweeper salesman. A traumatic experience. I remember it well. I was home alone sculpting my food when a solid rap at the door caused me to disfigure a bust of Marx I was molding from leftover pasta. A fine likeness, too. When I opened the door, there stood a sullen looking gentleman, stripped to the waist, wearing a bowler. In his hand was a complex looking item. He claimed it was one of his attachments. Being a naive child, I invited him into the house. An invitation which proved to be my undoing.

ADAMDONG. A deviate. Even at an early age.

OPHELIA. But I've always been a faithful and loyal companion.

ADAMDONG. Come now! How do you explain that incident in the motel?

OPHELIA. It was merely a lark.

ADAMDONG. And you consider it normal to have an affair with a bird?

OPHELIA. It flew up through the plumbing, and before I could react, the creature was upon me.

ADAMDONG. And then there was that nude woodsman in your bedroom.

OPHELIA. Was merely chopping down the four poster. Nothing more.

ADAMDONG. A nude woodsman cannot be trusted.

OPHELIA. To the contrary. The ones with the stocking caps, those are the ones that bear watching. What about the many nights you have returned home late? Have I ever questioned? And I've had many an occasion. You'll have to admit, Adamdong, the lipstick on your great toe wasn't my shade.

(ADAMDONG moves DOWNSTAGE and faces the audience, milk and sandwich in hand. As he speaks towards the audience, back to OPHELIA, a SAILOR ENTERS and begins to make love to OPHELIA.)

ADAMDONG. Living with a man of science, a man dedicated to research and discovery requires an enormous capacity for understanding. And I do appreciate your indulgence. Science is such a lonely life. *(The SAILOR continues to kiss and fondle OPHELIA behind the unsuspecting ADAMDONG. OPHELIA never stops ped-*

dling her Exercycle.) Today, for instance, I ranged far and wide only to uncover the carcass of a squirrel. And a gray squirrel at that. No doubt a victim of old age. Not exactly the ideal specimen for my research. But a man must make do, must not be defeated by the many obstacles that block his bid for greatness. Nothing can deter my studies, nothing will prevent me from realizing my dream. One day the name Adamdong Klosterhagen will emblazon the sky. Yes, on the whole, you have been an understanding help-mate. *(The SAILOR scurries from the Set.)* After all, a woman must be allowed a few inconsistencies.

OPHELIA. I could never be unfaithful to such an outstanding man of letters.

(ADAMDONG turns to a table and plunges his hand into a mountainous pile of envelopes.)

ADAMDONG. Yes, I have many letters from admirers everywhere.

OPHELIA. Well-wishers.

ADAMDONG. My heart glows when I read these beautiful words of encouragement.

OPHELIA. *(Resuming her knitting.)* Do read one.

ADAMDONG. Not wanting to play favorites, I'll select one at random. *(He turns his back to the table and dips his hand into the pile of envelopes, selecting one from the mountain. He removes a paper from the envelope and reads.)* "If your past due payment is not received by June 10th, your telephone service will be discontinued."

OPHELIA. Lovely.

ADAMDONG. *(Replacing the correspondence, selecting another.)* Cryptic, but touching. Some correspondents find it impossible to readily express their true admiration. The letters are encouraging. They spur me on.

OPHELIA. Your efforts are not for naught. Or is it—naught for not?

ADAMDONG. *(Ripping open another envelope.)* Note for note.

OPHELIA. Oh, yes.

ADAMDONG. *(Reads.)* "Dear Mr. Klosterhagen: Certain unusual information makes it necessary for us to question your form ten-forty. We have attempted to contact you by phone but apparently it is out of service. Therefore, I have directed our agent, Mr. William Koontz, to call upon you personally on Monday, June 19th. If this is not convenient, please contact me. Sincerely, Edward Hecht, Regional Director, IRS." *(He looks up.)* The nineteenth. That's today!

OPHELIA. What's IRS, dear?

ADAMDONG. International Research Scientists. My, what an honor.

OPHELIA. Coming to see you personally!

ADAMDONG. The word is spreading.

OPHELIA. It's hard to ignore true genius.

ADAMDONG. I must hasten to straighten the laboratory.

(Under dialogue ADAMDONG makes the following weird adjustments: turns the dental chair a quarter turn, straightens one picture, crumples up the sandwich wrapper, places it inside his hat and dons it.)

OPHELIA. Yes, we must prepare for such a distinguished guest. I have always known this moment would arrive.

ADAMDONG. Obviously the notes I sent to the foundation have created quiet a stir.

OPHELIA. I'll have to wear my new panty hose. The ones with the built in shoes.

ADAMDONG. I must be very careful not to let notoriety inter-
fere with my projects. A man must guard against social intrusions.
*(After donning his cap he looks about the room approvingly, as if
he's just painted it.)* Ah, that's better.

OPHELIA. Yes, I won't have to clean this week.

*(The DOCTOR ENTERS. He's a most befuddled looking gent.
wearing a dental smock.)*

DOCTOR. Good morning, Adamdong. Ophelia, my dear.

ADAMDONG & OPHELIA. Good morning, Doctor.

*(OPHELIA leaves her Exercycle and goes to the bar. As she crosses
in front of Milo she casually unzips his fly. He zips up mechanically.)*

OPHELIA. *(Pouring herself a drink.)* Sleep well?

DOCTOR. Quite. Dreamed I was a bowl of oatmeal. Interesting.

OPHELIA. I've had that dream. Was yours with cream and
sugar?

(She belts down the drink.)

DOCTOR. Skimmed milk.

*(Under dialogue the DOCTOR goes about the room casually
undoing ADAMDONG's work. He turns the dental chair back a
quarter turn, arranges the picture to its original crooked position. ADAMDONG struts about proselytizing regarding the
dream.)*

TO LIVE AT THE PITCH

ADAMDONG. A dream of Freudian complexity resulting from cataclysmic upheavals in the brain's cellular structure.

DOCTOR. Oh? Fascinating.

ADAMDONG. Merely interpretive analysis.

DOCTOR. Any patients?

OPHELIA. None as yet.

DOCTOR. *(Taking calling cards from his pocket.)* It's fluoridation! *(He hands OPHELIA a card.)* My card. The ruination of the dental practice. Too much prevention. *(Hands a card to ADAMDONG.)* Decay is becoming a thing of the past. Whatever happened to the toothache? I should have never turned from radiator repair to this profession.

ADAMDONG. One must not despair.

DOCTOR. Twenty years without a patient!

OPHELIA. These things take time. Like sex. It shouldn't be rushed. A few cocktails, fondling, dexterous manipulation of the sensitive areas... leg raises.

ADAMDONG. *(Aside to the DOCTOR.)* Her obsession with sex disturbs me.

OPHELIA. One day your office will be SRO.

DOCTOR. Hopefully.

ADAMDONG. But you have failed to realize the most monumental advance in dental science.

DOCTOR. What's that?

ADAMDONG. Advertising! A dentist must advertise. You need the newspapers, radio, television, direct mail, the Internet... a mass campaign. The name Otto P. Langworthy should be on the lips of every man, woman, and child.

DOCTOR. I'm not budgeted for advertising outlay.

ADAMDONG. Then how will the world ever know of your method of painful dentistry? You've got to bombard the marketplace. Advertising!

DOCTOR. They're all against me, that's the problem. Even in barber college where I was studying the effects of faulty follicle on the incisors I was ridiculed.

ADAMDONG. Your methods were too advanced. A pioneer must be prepared for adversities.

OPHELIA. But one day, when a patient comes, you'll be ready.

(She belts down a double.)

ADAMDONG. You must develop ad copy.

OPHELIA. Snappy one-liners.

DOCTOR. How about... "Dr. Otto P. Langworthy gives you gas!"

OPHELIA. It has a nice ring to it.

ADAMDONG. It might play.

OPHELIA. What about... "When in doubt—extract!"

ADAMDONG. "When you think of pain, think of Dr. Otto P. Langworthy."

DOCTOR. Perhaps the media is my answer.

ADAMDONG. No doubt. Then you must expand. Multiple offices. Then—franchises!

DOCTOR. A dental empire!

OPHELIA. You'll be on the big board. You can buy short and sell tall.

ADAMDONG. The prospects titillate the imagination.

OPHELIA. I was titillated once. In the rear seat of a limousine.

ADAMDONG. *(As a confidential aside to the DOCTOR.)* Again—sex. I fear philandering. *(Quickly returning to the subject at hand.)* Yes, a dynasty. Drive-in dentistry all over the land. "Stop at the sign of the Golden Bicuspid."

DOCTOR. "Over a hundred billion drilled!"

ADAMDONG. A modern entrepreneur must expand his base of operations. Must forge ahead boldly. Expansion. Moving outward from a central source, ever widening in vast concentric circles, dotting the globe like a profusion of fly diddle. First a subtle stubble, then a wisp of whiskers, then... a full beard! It's a universal law. *(He goes quickly to a large free-stranding blackboard, takes up chalk and begins to write as he speaks.)* First, a subtle stubble on the lip. *(He writes the word "lip" and underlines it.)* All right. And as any neophyte knows, the lip is over the chin. Right? *(He writes the word "chin" below the underline which is below the word " lip".)* Combine them, and you get the word... "lipchin." *(He makes an equals sign [=] to the right of the equation: lip over chin and then writes the word "lipchin.")* And as we all know, Lipchin is the name of the headwaiter at the China Nights restaurant. Right?

DOCTOR. Right.

ADAMDONG. And does he or does he not have a full-length beard.

DOCTOR. He does, most certainly.

ADAMDONG. Expansion! *(He boldly writes the word "expansion" on the board, drops the chalk into the tray and steps back dusting his hands authoritatively.)* I rest my case.

DOCTOR. Miraculous!

ADAMDONG. Simple logic.

OPHELIA. Another problem clarified in the light of pure reason.

(OPHELIA goes to the swing, sits and begins to pump.)

DOCTOR. I'll prepare a multi-media, mass-impact ad campaign at once. *(He whips out another calling card and hands it to ADAMDONG.)* My card.

ADAMDONG. Thank you. *(Crossing to the coat rack.)* Now I must spend a few moments with my precious friend. *(He removes MILO from the rack.)* Come, my little fellow.

TO LIVE AT THE PITCH

DOCTOR. Good morning, Milo.

ADAMDONG. *(Speaking for MILO, his mouth moving percep-tively.)* Good morning, Doctor.

DOCTOR. Splendid chap. I must check his teeth one day. No charge, of course.

(As ADAMDONG drags the limp figure of MILO to a chair the "dummy" mechanically belts the DOCTOR with his gloved hand, knocking the unsuspecting dentist to the floor.)

DOCTOR. Drat! Felled again by another sneaky punch.

(The DOCTOR gathers himself, nursing his jaw with his fingers.)

ADAMDONG. He has a devastating left hook. I've often con-sidered entering him in the welterweight division but I've never been able to find his other glove.

DOCTOR. Too bad. He's an obvious contender.

OPHELIA. Also a promiscuous mannequin.

(ADAMDONG sits in the chair, adjusts MILO on his knee.)

ADAMDONG. Now, there we are. Now, Milo, do you have a poem for us today?

(He answers his own question through the "dummy" his mouth moving obviously in synchronization with MILO's.)

> Otter tracks upon the snow
> Cause cold feet and nose to blow,
> Forty fathoms in the sand
> Making love to rubber band,

TO LIVE AT THE PITCH

Making friends that you can screw
Who can in turn do same to you,
Let's not waver from a stand
Except when gentiles form a band,
A little whore is short but nice
And only charges half the price,
May your socks rot in your shoes
If you ignore your union dues,
And... Pardon me boys but it's the Chattanooga choo-choo.

(MILO slumps forward.)

DOCTOR. Another enigmatic outpouring.
ADAMDONG. But profound!
DOCTOR. No doubt.
OPHELIA. A recondite little deviate. What does it all mean?

(Under dialogue ADAMDONG rises and places MILO in a chair.)

ADAMDONG. I must confess that even I, Adamdong
Klosterhagen, solver of universal riddles, find him impossibly abstruse. But none the less, I'm guided by his arcane offerings. This
limp little fellow is a true artist. He dips below the intellect into the
psychological well of imagery and symbolism. Combine this with a
solid left hook and you get—genius!
DOCTOR. One should never attempt to analyze true artistry.
OPHELIA. Accept in the bedroom.
DOCTOR. How goes your experiments, Adamdong?
ADAMDONG. I sense a breakthrough. Yesterday a hamster twittered under the voltage. I believe I've found the key.
DOCTOR. Really?

ADAMDONG. The key ingredient—Gin!

OPHELIA. Don't mind if I do.

ADAMDONG. I stumbled on it quite by accident. As is often the case with many important discoveries. Gillette, for instance, cutting himself while shaving; Madame Curie coming across Pierre giving an injection to a comely lab technician. Yes, accidents can result in monumental findings. *(He struts about, delivering his speech in a professorial manner.)* While running through my basic tests yesterday, I decided to indulge myself in a crispy Gibson. I prepared the drink carefully—a splash of vermouth to a beaker of gin, two onions. As I was lofting the crystal libation I was smitten by the pungent odor of anchovies wafting from the kitchen. I went to determine the source of the zephyr and, upon returning, inadvertently switched the Gibson with a beaker of nitric acid which, thankfully, I didn't ingest. At any rate, the Gibson proved to be the catalyst that caused the hamster to stir. Now I'm confident that I will realize my life's ambition of reviving a deceased animal.

DOCTOR. Wonderful!

OPHELIA. *(Swinging.)* Perhaps the delegate from the IRS will be present for the event.

DOCTOR. IRS?

ADAMDONG. Yes, Doctor. Due to "unusual information" contained in my notes, the International Research Scientists have determined to pay me a visit.

DOCTOR. A distinct honor. *(Clapping his hands.)* Perhaps he will have rotten teeth!

OPHELIA. Hopefully.

ADAMDONG. We'll pray for cavities. Yes, Doctor, today may be the day!

DOCTOR. How exciting! Have you chosen the lucky creature?

ADAMDONG. Yes. I think the squirrel. He has such a nice look about the mouth.

DOCTOR. A genuine event. I'll have to slip into a clean smock.

ADAMDONG. Do you realize what this will mean? I will be able to resurrect the greats of the animal kingdom.

OPHELIA. Lassie!

DOCTOR. Rin Tin Tin!

ADAMDONG. King Kong!

(Suddenly CALVIN bursts into the room. He's wearing a red, white, and blue beanie, a blue sweater with the white letters S H I T on its back and front, white pants, saddle shoes. He's carrying a red, white, and blue megaphone with the letters S H I T on it. He is an ebullient, exuberant, tumbling cheerleader. He tumbles forward and pops to his feet lithely, begins to lead a cheer. ADAMDONG, OPHELIA, and the DOCTOR fall into the spirit of the cheer with unbridled spontaneity and goodwill.)

CALVIN. *(Very Animated.)* Gimme an S—

ALL. S!

CALVIN. Gimme an H—

ALL. H!

CALVIN. Gimme an I—

ALL. I!

CALVIN. Gimme a T—

ALL. T! Yeeeeaaaaaaaaah! TEAM!

(CALVIN does a flip and bounds OFF STAGE. ADAMDONG, OPHELIA, the DOCTOR return to their former discussion as if nothing at all has transpired.)

ADAMDONG. Imagine the potentials. Why, the Museum of Natural History alone will occupy me for years. Mastodon, Pterodactyl, Dinosaur, Prehistoric man!

DOCTOR. *(Rubbing his hands with anticipatory glee.)* And women!

OPHELIA. I understand that the Neolithic period produced a most sensual species.

ADAMDONG. *(Aside to the DOCTOR.)* Again, a carnal reference. I suspect... *(Wobbling his hand from side to side.)* hanky-panky.

DOCTOR. *(Confidentially.)* It could be pressure from impacted wisdom teeth.

ADAMDONG. Hopefully that's the case.

DOCTOR. If they are not cut properly during the teens they can trigger peculiar behavior. There are numerous case histories. Napoleon, Freud, Martin Luther—all sufferers.

ADAMDONG. Really?

DOCTOR. There was the strange case of Fowler Freidman. His wisdom teeth acted as transistors resulting in television reception in his mouth. By the way, allow me to check your teeth. It will be good practice in the event the delegate from the IRS needs dental care.

ADAMDONG. Good thinking.

OPHELIA. Please feel free to inspect my cavity anytime.

(ADAMDONG and the DOCTOR exchange side-long glances. OPHELIA leaves the swing and goes to the bar. ADAMDONG climbs into the dental chair.)

ADAMDONG. Do you have floss?

DOCTOR. *(Going to a beat-up old cabinet.)* Oh yes, certainly. I always keep an ample supply. *(He opens the cabinet and withdraws a ball of twine which is at least a foot in diameter.)* A dentist would fairly flounder without a fullness of floss. Here we are.

ADAMDONG. It appears to be twine.

DOCTOR. Quite so. A patient tied down with floss can easily break free. Twine is much more satisfactory.

ADAMDONG. Of course.

OPHELIA. *(As she concocts a drink.)* I was tied down once and beaten by a maniac who had escaped from an institution in Macon, Georgia. He held me captive for days in a remote region of the Bayou country. As ransom he demanded a kaleidoscope of pornographic configurations. When the authorities finally complied with his outrageous demand he released me to wander about in snake-infested marshes. It was a harrowing experience that tattered three perfectly good hose. I've been a heavy drinker ever since.

(She belts down a double.)

DOCTOR. Was his name, Miller?

OPHELIA. Why, yes. Do you know of him?

DOCTOR. Myron Miller, the manic Macon misanthrope. Was recently a centerfold in a major magazine. He had a gigantic kaleidoscope. *(Addresses ADAMDONG.)* Open wide, please. *(He peers into Adamdong's mouth.)* Ah yes... Ummmmmmmm... Oh yes... Ah ha... Yesssss... Ah hummmmmmm.... *(As the Doctor oohs and ahs into Adamdong's mouth a DIPLOMAT ENTERS. He is dressed formally, is carrying a black attaché He goes to the foot of the dental chair, opens the attaché, removes shoe shine paraphernalia and begins to polish Adamdong's shoes. The others carry on oblivious to his presence.)* Ah yes, a fascinating mouth indeed! *(He inspects the interior of ADAMDONG's mouth with a dental mirror.)* It's obvious that you've recently eaten a Caesar salad. Right?

ADAMDONG. *(Answering awkwardly due to the instrument in his mouth.)* Uh huh.

DOCTOR. Just as I thought. Amazing! All the particles—the lettuce, anchovies, egg and croutons have melded into a mosaic-cyclorama of the Battle of Hastings.

OPHELIA. Really?

DOCTOR. Look for yourself.

OPHELIA. *(Peering into Adamdong's mouth.)* My! Truly an oral phenomenon!

(The DIPLOMAT, unnoticed, continues to shine ADAMDONG's shoes.)

DOCTOR. I'm sure the delegate from the IRS will be astounded.

OPHELIA. This will undoubtedly bring Adamdong even greater prestige.

DOCTOR. This mouth will win the Nobel Prize.

OPHELIA. More proof that research pays, that long hours of painstaking investigation is necessary to cogent revelations.

DOCTOR. *(Going for his camera.)* I must capture this on film.

ADAMDONG. *(Sitting upright.)* Is it truly glorious?

OPHELIA. Beautiful in every detail.

ADAMDONG. I owe it to proper mastication. I have always felt that one day correct eating habits would prove beneficial.

DOCTOR. *(Returning with a camera.)* Open wide. And smile!

(ADAMDONG leans back dramatically, mouth open wide. The DOCTOR brings the camera to eye level, focuses upon the open mouth. He drops the camera suddenly with an expression of despair.)

DOCTOR. It's gone!

OPHELIA. Gone!

ADAMDONG. *(Sitting up quickly.)* I must have swallowed inadvertently.

(The DIPLOMAT finishes the shine and begins to pack away his equipment.)

DOCTOR. He swallowed the Battle of Hastings.

OPHELIA. A bicarbonate at once!

ADAMDONG. How thoughtless of me. But even we scientists err upon occasion.

OPHELIA. None of us is perfect.

DOCTOR. Drat! And I had color film, too.

(The DIPLOMAT snaps shut his attaché, rises, hand extended.)

DIPLOMAT. Five dollars, please.

DOCTOR. *(Handing the diplomat his card.)* My card.

DIPLOMAT. Thank you.

ADAMDONG. *(Leaves the dental chair, handing the* DIPLO-MAT *two bucks.)* Don't despair, dear Doctor. Perhaps, after another Caesar, the scene will be recreated.

DIPLOMAT. Excuse me, sir, but it's time.

ADAMDONG. *(Checking his watch.)* So it is. Ophelia, Doctor, if you'll please excuse me. I have important documents to execute.

(ADAMDONG and the DIPLOMAT EXIT. The instant they leave the DOCTOR throws OPHELIA into the dental chair and begins to ravage her. It's a heated scene during which the DOCTOR's smock is ripped off revealing a giant tooth tattooed on his back.)

DOCTOR. Ophelia, my darling.

OPHELIA. Oh, Doctor.

DOCTOR. Ophelia, Ophelia.

OPHELIA. Doctor, Doctor.

DOCTOR. *(Coming up for air.)* I cannot contain my passion.

(Fairly leaping on her.) Kiss me again, my darling! *(They kiss.)* Again!

(They kiss again, heatedly.)

OPHELIA. It's the tattoo. It drives me wild!

(They kiss—wrestling about passionately—then break.)

DOCTOR. For years now we've been meeting like this. Always in secret.

OPHELIA. *(Rubbing the arms of the dental chair with nostalgic affection.)* If this dental chair could only talk.
DOCTOR. I don't know how much longer I can go on like this.
OPHELIA. It's torture.
DOCTOR. And it's ruining my practice.
OPHELIA. I know, I know.
DOCTOR. My love for you distracts me. I no longer care for my work. It's gotten to the point where I'm not even interested in a bad case of pyorrhea anymore. Extractions seldom enter my mind. Cavities are nothing. I may never be able to face another filling.
OPHELIA. Don't talk nonsense.
DOCTOR. *(He goes out of control.)* Our affair is driving me mad! Mad I say! MAD! I can't stand it any longer! I'm gong out of my mind! *(Coming apart. Screams madly.)* Yeeeeeeeeaaaaaaaaaah!
OPHELIA. Control yourself!
DOCTOR. Slap me! Slap me, quick!

(OPHELIA hauls off and belts him solidly, knocking him for a loop. There is a pause. Then the realization of pain sets in. The DOCTOR grabs his face, begins to writhe in pain.)

TO LIVE AT THE PITCH

DOCTOR. Oh! Ooooooooh! Ooooooooooow! Ouch!

OPHELIA. What is it, my dear?

DOCTOR. I think you've cracked a molar. *(Doubled in pain.)* Ooooooh! Oooooooow! Ahhhhhhhh! Ouch!

OPHELIA. Let's have a look. *(OPHELIA throws him into the dental chair roughly, peers into his mouth. The DOCTOR continues to moan with pain. Peering into the DOCTOR's mouth.)* Ah, yes. Hummm. Ah ha!

DOCTOR. What is it? What do you see?

OPHELIA. A molar is indeed cracked. We must extract at once.

DOCTOR. *(Rolling about in the chair, kicking like a child, holding his jaw.)* Oh no! No! Nooooooo! Ouch!

(OPHELIA begins to rout through the oddest assortment of "dental equipment" we've ever seen. Crude, rusty carpenters' and machinists' tools: saws, screw drivers, brace and bit, hammer, files, hand drills, speed wrenches and the like.)

OPHELIA. It will only take a minute. We'll have that tooth out in no time. *(She locates a large pair of rusty pliers.)* Now, open wide.

DOCTOR. *(He pulls away fearfully.)* No! I'm afraid! I want my mommy!

OPHELIA. Now now. We musn't panic. Open wide, please. *(Over the DOCTOR's protestations she forces open his mouth. To control his thrashing she places her knee in his chest and begins to pry the tooth from its moorings. The DOCTOR moans and groans, flailing wildly. Finally OPHELIA yanks the tooth free and stands back, proudly displaying the extracted molar in the pliers.)* There now, that wasn't so bad now, was it?

DOCTOR. *(Sitting up, nursing his jaw.)* Well... Well, no—No!

(Rotating his jaw, testing it.) Not bad at all. In fact, it was a very slick extraction. Very-slick-indeed.

OPHELIA. *(Holding out her palm.)* That will be six hundred dollars.

DOCTOR. What?!

OPHELIA. And fifty cents for the slap in the face.

DOCTOR. Six hundred dollars? Why, that's outrageous! You dentists are bilking the public!

OPHELIA. Sorry.

DOCTOR. Robbery! It isn't worth a penny over twelve ninety-five.

OPHELIA. Merely inflation. The cost of Novocaine, swabs... Prices have gone out of sight.

DOCTOR. You'll have to bill me.

OPHELIA. Fine. *(Handing him his smock.)* Here, put this on before Adamdong returns. Your appearance might arouse his suspicions.

DOCTOR. *(Rises. Dons his smock.)* For the life of me I can't understand how Adamdong can accuse you of being unfaithful.

(As OPHELIA speaks she goes to the bar and prepares herself a drink.)

OPHELIA. He's insanely jealous. He's been this way from the day we first met outside a public rest room in Chesterville. I had been there for several hours checking the flies of the gentlemen who were emerging from the facility. I've always been public spirited, you know. One cannot allow one's city streets to become infested with an army of unzipped executives, can one?

After several hours of conducting this benevolent activity, Adamdong stepped from the lavatory. He was wearing a morning suit, a properly adjusted homburg, spats, and was carrying a volume of Harrison's treatise on ferrets. His frontal area, however, was fully exposed. I discerned immediately that this was a man of enormous talents. When I discreetly approached him with the information that his trousers were gapping, he asked me to assist him in rectifying the problem behind a nearby hedge. I've been a heavy drinker ever since.

(She belts down the drink.)

> DOCTOR. It must be trying on you living with a man of genius.
> OPHELIA. Only during lent.
> DOCTOR. But now, apparently, after many years of laborious probing, he's on the threshold of discovery. His years of plodding are to be rewarded.
> OPHELIA. The hamster twittered. I saw it with my own eyes.
> DOCTOR. Witness to a miracle. *(ADAMDONG ENTERS.)* How goes it, Adamdong?
> ADAMDONG. Well, the documents are all signed and duly witnessed. A fresh pen for every page. And the lawyers were most helpful.

(OPHELIA seats herself on the Exercycle, honks its horn and starts pumping.)

> DOCTOR. Will they sue?
> ADAMDONG. Of course. They always sue.
> DOCTOR. Society is indebted to them all.
> ADAMDONG. *(Drawing the DOCTOR DOWNSTAGE confidentially.)* During my absence, did you discern anything... *(Wobbling his hand from side to side.)* irregular?
> DOCTOR. How so?
> ADAMDONG. Ophelia. Did she have an... *(Looking from side*

to side.) assignation?

(As ADAMDONG and the DOCTOR are huddling, a MARINE, dressed in his blues, ENTERS and begins to trifle with OPHELIA behind their backs.)

DOCTOR. Oh no. She was a pillar of chastity. Adamdong, allow me to speak freely as a friend and a medical man. I feel that you are siphoning valuable creative energies by dwelling upon these imaginary infidelities.

ADAMDONG. Perhaps. But I've been suspicious ever since an incident at Ridgefield Downs.

DOCTOR. Ridgefield Downs?

ADAMDONG. One Sunday, many years ago, Ophelia and I attended the polo matches there. It was an extremely hot afternoon and the gallery was perspiring profusely. Ophelia announced that she feared heat prostration and excused herself from the body of sweating fans. When, after more than an hour had elapsed and Ophelia had not yet returned to the stands, I began to fear for her well-being. Perhaps she had fallen victim to the soaring humidity which had become unbearable. One of the few times I've had to remove my spats. I departed the match—three to two, favor of Ridgefield—and began to scour the ground for my little darling. After much searching, I finally—much to my chagrin—came upon Ophelia in an abandoned stable.

DOCTOR. So?

ADAMDONG. *(Pulling the DOCTOR very close.)* She was in a compromising situation with a Dalmatian.

DOCTOR. No!

ADAMDONG. She maintained she was advancing the science of veterinary medicine.

DOCTOR. Well then, that explains it. Your mind should be free.

TO LIVE AT THE PITCH

(The MARINE scurries from the Set.)

ADAMDONG. Perhaps you're correct.

DOCTOR. After all, I am a medical man. People frequently give me as reference. Rest assured, Ophelia is steadfast in her commitment to such a great man of letters.

ADAMDONG. *(Turning toward the table.)* Have I read you my letters?

(Pulls an envelope from the pile.)

DOCTOR. Not recently.

ADAMDONG. Most uplifting communications. *(Pulling letter from the envelope. He reads.)* "If you do not remit eighty-nine dollars and eighty-eight cents by the tenth of the month, it will be necessary for us to place the matter in the hand of our collectors. Sincerely, Andrew McBride, credit department, Sears, Roebuck and Company."

DOCTOR. Wonderful!

ADAMDONG. Yes. Even the major corporations are becoming cognizant of my endeavors.

OPHELIA. *(Leaving the Exercycle.)* They're all climbing on the bandwagon now. But where were Mr. Sears and Mr. Roebuck when you were a young, struggling chemist.

ADAMDONG. Let's not be bitter.

DOCTOR. Yes. We must refrain from making disparaging remarks regarding one of the great capitalistic enterprises.

ADAMDONG. They have been known to give grants.

OPHELIA. I knew a Grant once. Lester Grant. Marvelous. The hair on his barrel-like chest had been marcelled.

ADAMDONG. *(Aside to the DOCTOR.)* Again her mind drifts

toward the sensual.

DOCTOR. The problem could be corrected with orthodontia.

(CALVIN bolts into the room, does a couple cartwheels and tumbles towards DOWNSTAGE where he invites the audience to participate in his cheer.)

CALVIN. *(To the audience.)* C'mon, everybody, let's give a great big rousing cheer for good ol' Stanley Hooker Institute of Technology! Let's hear it now.

(ADAMDONG, OPHELIA, and the DOCTOR fall into the spirit of the cheer. MILO also springs to life and participates.)

CALVIN. Gimme an S—
EVERYBODY. S!
CALVIN. Gimme an H—
EVERYBODY. H!
CALVIN. Gimme an I—
EVERYBODY. I!
CALVIN. Gimme a T—
EVERYBODY. T! Yeeeeeaaaahhhhh—TEAM!

(CALVIN leads applauding, whistling, foot-stomping. Then he flip-flops exuberantly from the stage. MILO slumps into the chair, once again an emotionless mannequin. ADAMDONG, OPHELIA, and the DOCTOR continue their dialogue as it nothing has transpired.)

ADAMDONG. *(Moving the dental chair a quarter turn, straightening crooked photograph.)* The charitable spirit of the major corporations cannot be ignored. Their generosity sustains the creative artist and advances significant research. Why, this year alone, General Motors has donated thirty-six dollars and fifty cents, General Electric thirteen ninety-five.

OPHELIA. It adds up.

ADAMDONG. And all this in view of a sagging fiscal picture.

DOCTOR. I saw that picture. Not bad for a musical.

ADAMDONG. We must never lose sight of our benefactors.

DOCTOR. Or of a good set of x-rays. Have you seen my latest?

(He reaches into the pocket of his smock and removes x-rays.)

OPHELIA. *(Approaching.)* No.

ADAMDONG. Are these the ones from our last party?

DOCTOR. I picked them up yesterday.

(ADAMDONG and OPHELIA crowd in around the DOCTOR as he holds up the x-rays to the light for viewing.)

DOCTOR. Here's a lovely series of a root canal.

ADAMDONG. Excellent.

OPHELIA. Lovely.

DOCTOR. And look at this classic example of periodontal neglect.

ADAMDONG. Ah!

OPHELIA. Please order me a set. Wallet size. Tinted.

ADAMDONG. And a few five-by-sevens for the family.

DOCTOR. *(Holding up what appears to be photographs.)* And I particularly like these shots of... *(Drops them quickly, obviously embarrassed.)* Oh my! Excuse me. I'm terribly sorry. How'd these get in here?

OPHELIA. Why, Doctor!

ADAMDONG. A most flagrant exposé.

DOCTOR. *(Quickly returning the photos to his pocket.)* No doubt a, a mix up at the developers.

OPHELIA. Utterly disgusting.

ADAMDONG. Indeed. *(Checking his wrist-watch.)* Enough of this. I must prepare for my experiment.

DOCTOR. Yes... the experiment!

(As the DOCTOR turns, OPHELIA deftly pilfers the photos from his pocket and places them under her shirt.

ADAMDONG. This time I'm confident there will be a major breakthrough.

OPHELIA. The hamster twittered.

DOCTOR. Your pragmatism is about to be rewarded.

ADAMDONG. *(Going to the refrigerator.)* I must select the lucky creature.

OPHELIA. *(Pouring herself a stiff drink.)* A difficult choice.

ADAMDONG. Yes. I've grown quite fond off all my little pets. I'd like to resuscitate them all simultaneously but, unfortunately, that's quiet impossible. *(He opens the refrigerator door.)* Now... let me see.

(OPHELIA and the DOCTOR huddle near the open refrigerator as ADAMDONG routs through the frozen animals.)

OPHELIA. Why not the hamster?

DOCTOR. Yes, he twittered.

ADAMDONG. No. I'm afraid the last session had a detrimental effect upon his fur. Beer, Doctor?

DOCTOR. Why, yes. Perhaps a libation will serve to lessen the tension of the moment.

(ADAMDONG removes a can of beer from the fridge, pops its top and hands it to the DOCTOR, resumes digging through the stiffs. He takes the squirrel from the box.)

ADAMDONG. It shall be... be—the squirrel!
OPHELIA. An excellent choice. *(She and the DOCTOR peer at the stiff squirrel in ADAMDONG's hand.)* Amazing. He bears a distinct resemblance to a Czechoslovakian I once dated. Was a pole vaulter. Marvelous staff.

(OPHELIA belts down her drink. ADAMDONG and the DOCTOR share side-long glances. ADAMDONG breaks and carries the squirrel to the operating table, DOCTOR and OPHELIA in his wake. He places the animal carefully on the table and begins to systematically attach electrodes to its carcass.)

ADAMDONG. I shall breathe precious life back into this miserable rodent; will restore him fully. His vital juices will once again surge through his furry little frame.
DOCTOR. He appears to have nicotine stains on his incisors. Apparently was a heavy smoker.
OPHELIA. It's high-time you were rewarded, Adamdong. You've been a diligent campaigner. You've worked nights, Sundays, with not even a minute off for golf.
ADAMDONG. My back-swing has become atrocious. Yes, this fuzzy little fellow will soon stand bushy-tailed as a marvel of science. You know, I have often been tempted to abandon my pursuits. And upon many occasions friends, concerned for my well-being, have attempted to dissuade me. But I have remained resolute with a commitment to the real values.

(ADAMDONG crosses to the bar.)

DOCTOR. Credit cards.

ADAMDONG. Yes. *(Holds up a bottle of gin.)* Gin! The key ingredient!

OPHELIA. I've always thought so. *(ADAMDONG returns to the table and proceeds to measure a strange concoction into a blender. A dab of this, a smidgen of that, a dribble, a squirt, a jigger, a drop of various and sundry liquids. OPHELIA and the DOCTOR look on intently as ADAMDONG measures and pours with great precision and concentration. OPHELIA withdraws to a position slightly to the side of and behind the two men, slyly pulls the questionable photos from beneath her shirt and holds them to the light for viewing. Hovering over ADAMDONG.)* Amazing!

OPHELIA. *(Ogling the photos.)* Yes!

DOCTOR. Astounding!

OPHELIA. Most astounding!

DOCTOR. The method is most unique.

OPHELIA. *(Noting the negatives, eyes bulging.)* Not to mention the positions!

DOCTOR. *(Leaning in over ADAMDONG as he mixes.)* I've never seen anything like this.

OPHELIA. *(With look of ecstasy.)* Nor I!

DOCTOR. Such scope.

OPHELIA. Not to mention size!

ADAMDONG. And now.... *(He laces the mixture with a healthy slug of gin, slaps the top on the container and hits the blender's start button. OPHELIA quickly conceals the photos. They all stand as the blender whips the mixture to a thick, murky consistency. After a few seconds, ADAMDONG switches off the blender, removes the container and holds it aloft triumphantly with a look of glazed madness.)* And now... the elixir of life! *(He pours a portion of the glop*

TO LIVE AT THE PITCH

into a funnel that is raised about two feet above the table. Descending from the bottom of the funnel is a length of plastic tubing that connects to the squirrel by means of a hypodermic needle. After pouring, ADAMDONG stands back, rubbing his hands together with gleeful satisfaction. OPHELIA snatches up the bottle of gin and takes a gigantic swig.) We're ready! Stand back everyone!

(MILO comes to life and joins the others who show no reaction to his presence. With a dramatic, sweeping gesture, ADAMDONG throws a huge breaker switch at the side of the operating table. The Set LIGHTS DIM under the power surge and motors whir, beakers bubble, wheels spin, gears mesh, electrodes crackle and neon tubes radiate eerie hues. Then a shower of sparks erupts, bathing the set in a silver waterfall of shimmering electricity. Then: a theatre-shaking explosion. Kaboom!)

BLACKOUT

END OF ACT I

TO LIVE AT THE PITCH

ACT II

Scene 1

(The room is in the same disheveled state. MILO is back on the coat rack. VOICES OFF are heard approaching. ADAMDONG and PASCAL DILLDAY ENTER. PASCAL is a six foot squirrel. He is a very debonair, intelligent, jaunty, self-assured raconteur. He's smoking a huge cigar, carrying a golf club, a Wall Street Journal tucked under one arm. There is a watch fob strung across his stomach with ends disappearing into slits in his fur. PAS-CAL has an arm around ADAMDONG's shoulders in a manner of great camaraderie.)

PASCAL. We must always be aware of the small investors.

ADAMDONG. Midgets.

PASCAL. Right. And Jockeys. The small investor often displays outstanding acumen. I was once acquainted with a pair of dwarfs who were most astute regarding market manipulations.

ADAMDONG. Crafty little devils.

PASCAL. They fared well during the crash.

ADAMDONG. 1929?

PASCAL. Oh no. 1999, on the freeway. It was a black day for the Standard and Poors. Market bottomed out. I remember it well. *(As he speaks, he casually goes to the dental chair and moves it a quarter turn and then readjusts the photo to crooked position.)* I was residing in Wales at the time. Ran a little haberdashery there. Specialized in exquisite cravats. Business was bullish and over-the-counter sales were brisk. This was during my fourth reincarnation. Things were going marvelously and I was speculating heavily in untested stocks: a rubber band plantation, a waffle ranch, an organic contraceptive device, a hair pomade concocted from ginseng root. Yes, I was plunging to say the least. And—if I must say so myself— my investments were paying off handsomely. Incidentally... I had a seat on the exchange.

ADAMDONG. Really?

PASCAL. A very plush reclining model with a built-in vibrator. It had my name, Pascal Dillday, prominently embroidered across its back. I exchanged it later for a chaise lounge.

ADAMDONG. The market served you well.

PASCAL. Then one day, while instructing a customer regarding the proper construction of a Windsor knot, the Dow Jones plummeted leaving me penniless. I was forced to sell my set of matched woods.

(Swings the golf club in a wide arc.)

ADAMDONG. I know only too well that abysmal feeling. I was once forced to sell a perfectly good set of hypodermic needles to a strange looking fellow with amplified musical equipment.

PASCAL. But that was in my forth life. Now, thanks to your innate genius, here I am back considering blue chip issues once again. How can I ever repay you?

ADAMDONG. Perhaps an inside tip.

PASCAL. *(Very confidential, leaning in close.)* Okra.

ADAMDONG. Okra?

PASCAL. *(Finger to his lips.)* Sssssssh! *(Glancing from side to side.)* One can't be too careful. Yes, okra. Look for a great international upsurge in gumbo.

ADAMDONG. Ahhhhhh. Pascal, you are truly a marvel. I had a special feeling about you from the first. My intuition led me to select you over the other creatures.

PASCAL. My good fortune. And now, you'll be famous.

ADAMDONG. Yes. I expect a delegate from the IRS today.

PASCAL. *(Moving to the bar.)* They chose an opportune time for the visit. Martini?

ADAMDONG. Extra dry, with a twist.

PASCAL. *(He begins to prepare the martinis.)* Ah! The way we used to drink them at the club. Yes, lucky indeed for me that I was pulled from a pile of dead leaves by Adamdong Klosterhagen. Had you not stumbled upon me when you did, my tissue would have deteriorated beyond repair. Ah! Resurrected again. Marvelous!

ADAMDONG. Your experiences must be fascinating. Spanning hundreds of years.

PASCAL. It all began in the early fifteen hundreds. I was a sculptor, specializing in bas-relief. Then I met Michaelangelo.

ADAMDONG. He made an exquisite marinara sauce.

PASCAL. The finest if Italy before he went commercial. I worked for Mike for many years. Managed the Genoa branch of his restaurant chain. Everything was going beautifully until he became obsessed with the ceiling in the Sistine Chapel. He spent weeks on end studying crevasses and undulations.

(Hands ADAMDONG a martini.)

ADAMDONG. An Italian girl?

PASCAL. No no! Mike was... *(Hand from side to side, with a wink.)* you know. After that, everything began to go down hill. His involvement ruined his profit picture.

ADAMDONG. Yes, I've seen that picture. One of his lesser

works.

PASCAL. Sad. His mania for the ceiling destroyed his posture. After awhile he could only look up.

ADAMDONG. Pity.

PASCAL. When he finally decided to tackle the monumental task of embellishing the dome he employed me as his first assistant. Being union we hastily completed the job in several years. *(Confidential.)* Contrary to common opinion, it was roller coated.

(He struts about handsomely, puffing his cigar, sipping his martini.)

ADAMDONG. Water base, or oil?

PASCAL. White clam sauce shaded to varying degrees with burnt umber.

ADAMDONG. Of course.

PASCAL. Then, in my next life, I proofread for Shakespeare.

ADAMDONG. A lousy speller, I understand.

PASCAL. And the man never finished a thing. He was always too occupied with fund raisings.

ADAMDONG. But a genius.

PASCAL. No doubt. After all, he initiated the subscription season.

ADAMDONG. Then how does one account for his enormous output? Christopher Marlowe?

PASCAL. No.

ADAMDONG. Then— *(Realization.)* Then— *(With a knowing finger at PASCAL.)* YOU!

PASCAL. Right! *(Extends a proud paw.)* Shake the hand, that held the quill that wrote the stuff, and signed it—Bill!

ADAMDONG. *(Shaking PASCAL's paw enthusiastically.)* Well, I'll be. So you're the one. Well, I'll be.

PASCAL. Always had a way with words. A knack, you know.

Yes, I've enjoyed some exciting occupations. But none as reward-
ing as my last, however.

ADAMDONG. And that was?...

PASCAL. TV repair.

ADAMDONG. An important social contribution. Commendable.

PASCAL. *(Waving off the compliment.)* No kudos, please.

ADAMDONG. I understand.

PASCAL. *(Pulling pocket watch from his fur.)* We must keep a
close eye on the time. The market will be closing soon.

ADAMDONG. Hopefully... *(The word "okra" sotto voce.)* okra
will close up.

*(OPHELIA and the DOCTOR ENTER and ad lib salutations are
exchanged. All are in high spirits. OPHELIA is carrying her
pumpkin.*

DOCTOR. A banner day!

OPHELIA. Congratulations, Adamdong.

DOCTOR. *(Handing his card to PASCAL.)* My card.

(He hands out cards to ADAMDONG and OPHELIA.)

ADAMDONG. *(Patting the pumpkin.)* Why hello there,
Henrietta.

DOCTOR. *(Alternately shaking ADAMDONG's and PASCAL's
hands.)* We always knew your persistence would be rewarded.

PASCAL. Truly a scientific landmark.

(OPHELIA places the pumpkin in the basket on the Exercycle.)

ADAMDONG. I owe it all to early potty training.

(CALVIN tumbles into the room. He evokes cheers from ADAMDONG, OPHELIA, DOCTOR, PASCAL and the audience.)

CALVIN. C'mon, everybody, three cheers for Adamdong! Hip hip—
EVERYBODY. Hooray!
CALVIN. Hi hip—
EVERYBODY. Hooray!
CALVIN. Hip hip—
EVERYBODY. Hooray!

(Whistles, screams, shouts, foot stomping.)

CALVIN. Speech!
DOCTOR, OPHELIA,
CALVIN, PASCAL. Yes. Speech. Speech. Yes. Speech. Speech. Speech, Adamdong!

(They whistle, stamp and applaud, coaxing the audience to join in.)

ADAMDONG. *(Calming them, going to the coat rack.)* All right, all right. Perhaps a speech is in order. I'll speak through my profound little friend.

(OPHELIA pours herself a drink, PASCAL seats himself in the dental chair as ADAMDONG takes MILO from the rack.)

OPHELIA. The dummy is indeed a marvel.
DOCTOR. The marionette mellifluously mouths meaty mental morsels.

TO LIVE AT THE PITCH

(As ADAMDONG drags MILO past the DOCTOR, the dummy knocks him to the floor with his gloved hand. ADAMDONG sits in chair and adjusts MILO on his knee. Then he speaks through him, same voice, mouth obviously moving all over his face:)

ADAMDONG. *(Clears throat.)* Ladies and gentlemen—
ALL. Wonderful. Eloquent. Beautiful. Poetry. More, more... [etc.]
ADAMDONG. Ladies and gentlemen. It is a distinct pleasure to be called upon to address such an august body.
OPHELIA. *(Running her hands down her torso as she wriggles coquettishly.)* Why, thank you.
ADAMDONG. We have seen many atrocities; have witnessed the carnage of foolish wars; have been subjected to stupidity, waste, disease, taxes, tariffs, and floods. And allow me to say this about that... Our boys will never fight on foreign soil.
CALVIN. How about that, folks?

(Evokes whistles, screams, cheers, shouts, applause from the cast and audience.)

ADAMDONG. It has been a long and arduous campaign fraught with diplomatic complexities. But, let me assure you, never again will our diplomats shilly-shally or dilly-dally at a political rally! Often, as I have traveled this great land of ours, I have witnessed the ravages of indecisive government; have perceived pockets of pitiful pestilence. But, I have taken steps to rectify the situation. I am eliminating—paperwork!
CALVIN. Let's hear it for a great humanitarian!

(Leads cheering, shouting , etc.)

ADAMDONG. And in honor of this auspicious event, I am declaring today and every June nineteenth henceforth—Pascal Dillday Day! Thank you.

(CALVIN leads audience and cast in foot-stomping, shouting and applause. ADAMDONG alternately bows graciously to the cast and audience, basking in kudos. Then he replaces MILO on the coat rack. As he drags the dummy past OPHELIA, she unzips his fly.)

OPHELIA. Beautiful, Adamdong.
DOCTOR. Truly inspirational.
PASCAL. A true patriot.
DOCTOR. And expressed so concisely and with such clarity of thought.

(MILO zips up.)

ADAMDONG. I had an uncle who was an evangelist.
PASCAL. That explains it.

(CALVIN sits in the swing, OPHELIA mounts the Exercycle, honks horn and begins to pedal.)

DOCTOR. *(Scrutinizing PASCAL's mouth.)* My, what an interesting pair of centrals.
PASCAL. *(Opening his mouth wide, pointing to his teeth.)* I owe it all to fluoridation.
OPHELIA. Fornication?

(ADAMDONG and the DOCTOR exchange side-long glances.)

TO LIVE AT THE PITCH

ADAMDONG. *(Into PASCAL's ear.)* She often alludes to the flesh. I suspect...

(Wobbling his hand from side to side.)

PASCAL. Indeed? Recalls to mind a young lady I once encountered in Amsterdam. *(ADAMDONG and the DOCTOR move in close on PASCAL. CALVIN leaves the swing and joins the huddle.)* I met her one winter's eve while skating on the river.

ADAMDONG. Zuider Zee?

PASCAL. *(Confidential.)* You should have zeen 'er zuider. *(Oohs and ahs from his listeners.)* I was skimming over the ice at a blistering pace, my blades glinting in the moonlight, when suddenly I came upon a young lady with her finger in a dyke. Her name was Gretchen Brinker. Wife of none other than you-know-who. *(Again oohs and ahs.)* There was an immediate animal attraction between us and I hastened to invite her to my flat for a warming dram of a very potent liquor which I maintained for such emergencies. *(Interrupts his story.)* Just a moment. *(He pulls the watch from his fur and notes the time.)* The market will close soon. *(Back to his story.)* Well, we repaired to my lodgings and proceeded to reduce the contents of the bottle to mere dregs. An act which served to loosen both Mrs. Brinker's tongue and morals. *(Oohs and ahs.)* She related how her husband's skating obsession had negatively affected their sexual relationship. In fact, she confided, during their last intimacy he had made figure-eighths on her stomach during the entire incident.

ADAMDONG. A true athlete.

PASCAL. Normally, mind you, I would never take advantage of a lady whose senses had been addled due to over-imbibing.

ADAMDONG. Of course not.

DOCTOR. It goes without saying.

PASCAL. But, in view of Mrs. Brinker's depressed state, gentlemen, what else could I do?

ADAMDONG. Nothing.

DOCTOR. You were only being humane.

ADAMDONG. Magnanimous.

PASCAL. It was a most unusual and painful experience.

ADAMDONG. How so?

PASCAL. She refused to remove her wooden shoes. *(Rises and points to his back.)* I still carry splinters to this day.

(The men inspect PASCAL's wounds, oohing and ahing.)

PASCAL. Let me ask you, Adamdong, have you noticed the presence of splinters on or about the persons of Ophelia's male friends and/or acquaintances?

ADAMDONG. No, I can't say that I have.

PASCAL. Well then, you have nothing to fear. *(Pulls the watch from his fur and notes the time.)* Ah! The market has closed. Time to check the reports. *(Heading for EXIT.)* Come, gentlemen.

(ADAMDONG, the DOCTOR and CALVIN follow PASCAL from the room. As soon as they have exited, OPHELIA lifts the top from the pumpkin, pulls a pint of gin from it and takes a manly slug. The doorbell sounds. OPHELIA replaces the gin inside the pumpkin and crosses to the door which she flings open revealing BILL KOONTZ, representative from the IRS. He is a straight-laced, colorless, humorless, all business guy of grim determination. He is wearing a three-piece polyester suit, wing-tip shoes, a fifty-cent necktie. Firmly in hand is an attaché case. OPHELIA begins to flirt with him unabashedly.)

OPHELIA. Why, hello. Just in time for a drink.

TO LIVE AT THE PITCH

BILL. I beg your pardon.

(OPHELIA grabs BILL by the sleeve and jerks him into the room.)

OPHELIA. You timing is perfect. The others have repaired to the other room to check the market results. It'll only take me a moment to remove my clothing.
BILL. What?
OPHELIA. Let's not be shy.

(OPHELIA deftly unzips his fly causing him to jump back with alarmed embarrassment.)

BILL. What the hell you think you're doing? *(Zipping up behind his attaché case.)* I'm a... a... I'm aGovernment Man!
OPHELIA. Ah, a diplomat! They always wear white gloves during sex. Most sanitary.
BILL. *(Heading for the door, bumbling.)* L—look miss, ya—you got the wrong guy. *(Backing toward the door.)* I—I'm in the wrong house, okay? *(Opening the door, backing out.)* Sorry I bothered you. I was looking for the Klosterhagen residence. Bye.

(Begins to close the door.)

OPHELIA. Adamdong Klosterhagen?
BILL. *(Through a crack in the door.)* Yes, that's right.
OPHELIA. He's tied up at the moment. Okra, you know.
BILL. *(Opening the door slightly.)* You mean, this is the right house?
OPHELIA. It is indeed. Enter, my good man. Don't dilly-dally on the stoop. *(BILL ENTERS cautiously.)* Who shall I say is calling?
BILL. *(Drinking in the weird surroundings with a look of incre-*

dulity.) Huh? Oh! Oh, yes... *(Whips an I. D. from his pocket.)* Tell 'im Bill Koontz, IRS.

OPHELIA. IRS? Why didn't you say so? We've been expecting you! My, what a distinct honor. Adamdong is absolutely thrilled about your visit.

BILL. Thrilled?

OPHELIA. He's been talking of nothing else since receiving the communiqué from your superior.

BILL. Are you Mrs. Klosterhagen?

OPHELIA. *(Extending her hand.)* Ophelia Rass.

BILL. *(Quickly covering his backside with his attaché case.)* I beg your pardon?

(OPHELIA grabs BILL's lapels and jerks him close and speaks to him with an air of utmost confidentiality. Bill, disarmed, stares at her bug-eyed.)

OPHELIA. Mr. Koontz, I want you to know that I've stood by Adamdong throughout his years of lonely experimentation. I have never wavered. Except on one occasion with a dashing plumber's helper.

BILL. But... but....

OPHELIA. *(Drawing him closer.)* It's not easy living with a man of genius. Great attrition on the moral fibers, you know. This pressurized environment has reduced me to easy prey for philanderers. You're not a philanderer, are you?

BILL. *(Wide-eyed.)* Of Course not! I'm U. S. of A.!

OPHELIA. Thank heavens! *(Jerking him closer.)* I was once held captive in a seedy motel—not recommended by the Auto Club— by a smooth-shaven civil engineer who importuned me to commit unspeakable acts. *(She smiles insanely, savoring the memory.)* He plundered me for two days before releasing me to wander aimlessly on foreign fens. I've been a heavy drinker ever since. *(She shoves him away gruffly.)* How dare you force me to reveal my intimate past?

BILL. What?! Now see here, Miss...

OPHELIA. Rass.

BILL. Whatever. I'm not the least bit interested in your sordid past. I'm here on official business.

(Flashes his ID.)

OPHELIA. IRS.

BILL. Exactly.

OPHELIA. I understand fully the nature of your business.

BILL. *(Straightening his lapels, tie, shoring himself up, very proper.)* Good. So let's keep it on a professional level, okay?

OPHELIA. I once attempted it on a professional level, but we kept rolling out of bed. *(Going to bar.)* A refreshment perhaps?

BILL. I never drink on duty.

OPHELIA. Most commendable.

BILL. *(Proudly displaying a lapel pin.)* I have a twenty year pin. Full retirement at age fifty-five. And not one evader has ever slipped through my fingers. Not a bad record, if I do say so myself.

OPHELIA. *(Fixing a drink.)* I've never heard that record.

BILL. Huh?

OPHELIA. I abandoned music after my accordion instructor forced me to give him a private recital in the nude. I still carry the marks on my stomach. See for yourself.

(Begins to raise her baseball uniform.)

BILL. Stop that!

(She drops the uniform.)

BILL. Now look here, Miss... Miss...

OPHELIA. Rass.

BILL. Yes. Whatever. I don't know what your game is but—

OPHELIA. It's strip poker. And I'm a good loser.

BILL. Look, if you're trying to rattle me, forget it. I'm a seasoned veteran. *(Pushing out his lapel pin.)* Twenty years! Nothing gets in my way. I never stray from my path. I always get my man.

OPHELIA. Funny, you don't appear to be homosexual.

BILL. *(With a nervous twitch.)* What?

OPHELIA. Although one never knows these days. Just last week I saw a truck driver walking with a lisp.

BILL. I don't know what in the world you're talking about.

OPHELIA. Now, now, let's not be coy.

(Throws back the drink.)

BILL. Whadaya mean?

OPHELIA. After all, the hamster twittered.

BILL. What?

OPHELIA. *(Most confidential.)* And then... Pascal.

BILL. Now look, Miss, Miss what's-yer-name...

OPHELIA. Rass.

BILL. Whatever. I don't know about any hamsters or any Pascals. All I know is that I'm here to see an Adamdong Klosterhagen about his ten-forty.

OPHELIA. *(Hands about a foot apart.)* It used to be a full eleven inches.

BILL. *(Impatient, advancing on OPHELIA waving his finger admonishingly.)* You'd better watch it, you're fooling around with Uncle Sam! *(As BILL crosses in front of MILO the dummy decks*

him with a lightening left. BILL hits the floor, attaché case flying.
He points at MILO hysterically.) It hit me! It hit me! *(Scrambling to*
his feet, pointing feverishly at the lifeless figure of MILO on the
rack.) The dummy hit me!

OPHELIA. Please, Mr. Cunts.

BILL. Koontz! I saw him! I saw him!

OPHELIA. *(Patting MILO on the head.)* It's merely a dummy.

BILL. It hit me, I'm telling you, it hit me! He, he has no right
touching me, no right! *(Twitches.)* I'M CIVIL SERVICE!

OPHELIA. Please. Relax. Take a seat while I summon
Adamdong.

(OPHELIA makes a cross toward door. As she passes MILO she
casually unzips his fly. She EXITS. BILL retrieves his attach?
case and walks about the room surveying the nutty accouter-
ments, the wild and off-beat paraphernalia. He looks MILO over
thoroughly, peering intently into his face. MILO is motionless,
glassy-eyed. As BILL turns away, MILO zips up. BILL, catching
this from the corner of his eye, spins about quickly. MILO is
again a cold, emotionless figure. BILL stalks the room, mutter-
ing:)

BILL. A bunch of evaders live here, bet on it. Just look at this
place. A front if I've ever seen one. And this Ophelia what's-'er-
name, trying to throw me off the scent. What a laugh. Nobody throws
ol' ten-forty Bill Koontz off— nobody. These people probably owe
back taxes for thirty years. Just wait'll I get through with 'em. *(No-*
ticing the "formula" on the blackboard.) Ah ha! A secret formula. A
code! I've stumbled into something big here! *(CALVIN careens into*
the room, does a couple of flip-flops, startling BILL.) Who... who
are you?

CALVIN. I'm Calvin, sir.

BILL. *(Aside to audience.)* Another evader.

CALVIN. Who are you?

BILL. *(Flashing his ID pompously.)* IRS! Have a seat, kid, I wanna ask you a few questions.

CALVIN. Yes, sir.

(CALVIN does a flip and lands in the dental chair. BILL pulls a note pad and a pen from his pocket. He stiffens, clears his throat. Very pompous and very professional.)

BILL. Now, what's you full name?

CALVIN. Calvin Christ.

BILL. *(Begins to write.)* Calvin Christ. *(Catches himself.)* Hey! Watch it, kid.

CALVIN. Yes, sir.

BILL. *(Twitches, clears his throat.)* And your age?

CALVIN. Two thousand two hundred seven.*

(*NOTE: update in the interest of chronological correctness.)

BILL. This is serious stuff, buddy, so watch your answers. Now, last year what was your total income derived from wages, tips and other employee compensation?

CALVIN. Thirty-eight cents.

BILL. What?!

CALVIN. I'm sorry... thirty-nine.

BILL. What's your occupation?

CALVIN. Cheerleader.

BILL. *(His twitches becoming more frequent.)* Don't lie to me.

CALVIN. I have a Masters in cheerleading.

BILL. *(Shaking his note pad.)* Watch it! These are multiple copies!

TO LIVE AT THE PITCH

CALVIN. I did my paper on cheerleading, sir. I titled it— *(He bounds from the dental chair and delivers the title in cheerleader fashion.)* "Rah, Rah, Siss Boom Bah, Boom-a-laka, Boom-a-laka, Rah Rah Rah!"

BILL. I'm warning you, pal!

CALVIN. *(Pointing for BILL's attaché case.)* What you got in the case, mister?

BILL. *(Pulling the case away protectively.)* Stay away from this!

(Twitch.)

CALVIN. *(Reaching out for the case.)* Can I see it?

BILL. *(Recoiling, hugging the case.)* Look, punk, don't you dare lay a finger on this case. *(Frenzy mounting.)* Do you realize there are GOVERNMENT FORMS IN HERE!

CALVIN. *(Advancing.)* Are you okay, mister?

BILL. *(Jumping back as if CALVIN were a leper.)* I'm fine. Get away from me. *(CALVIN backs off.)* Now, answer me quick! What's Lipchin?

CALVIN. The head waiter at the China Nights.

BILL. *(Aside to audience.)* Ah ha! Oriental tax evaders! *(CALVIN flip-flops from the room.)* Hey! Where you think you're going? Come back here! *(He slumps into the dental chair, withdraws a handkerchief from his pocket and begins to mop his forehead.)* The kid couldn't stand the pressure. My interrogation got too hot for 'im. Probably an Asian tax evader the way he bounces around. They all have great balance.

(He relaxes in the chair, mopping his brow. The DOCTOR ENTERS and spots him. His face becomes radiant.)

DOCTOR. *(Aside, sotto voce to the audience.)* Ah, a patient at last.

*(The DOCTOR silently tip-toes behind the unsuspecting BILL and
    quietly removes the ball of twine from the cabinet. He unravels
    a lengthy portion and sneaks up behind BILL, twine at the ready.
    Then, with a quick, positive move, he flips the twine over BILL
    and pins him to the chair. BILL, startled emits a horrendous
    scream and attempts to jump from the chair. But he's captive.
    The DOCTOR winds the twine tightly around the screaming,
    struggling BILL pinning him securely.)*

BILL. *(Screaming, kicking, floundering like fish on deck.)* Stop
it! Stop it, dammit! What the hell you think you're doing? Let me
outta here! Let me go! Let me go, I say! *(The DOCTOR runs in
circle around the chair constricting BILL more securely with each
revolution.)* Stop it, I say! You're under arrest! You'll pay for this!
Damn you! Let me outta this chair! You hear me, you crazy bastard?
Let me go, I say! You're gonna pay for this, you son of a bitch.
You're messing with GOVERNMENT PROPERTEEEEEEEE!

*(The DOCTOR spots BILL's handkerchief on the floor, picks it up
    and shoves it into BILL's mouth. He stands back, dusts his hands
    over a job well done. BILL flounders, a helpless, muted indi-
    vidual.)*

DOCTOR. Relax, my good man, we'll have those teeth out in
no time at all.

*(BILL kicks and flails, his eyes bug as the DOCTOR begins to rout
    through his odd assortment of instruments: saw, hammer, chisel,
    brace & bit, hatchet, etc.)*

TO LIVE AT THE PITCH

DOCTOR. You won't feel a thing. I'll anesthetize you by applying a subtle pressure to your lumbar area. A method perfected by Dr. Harishna Henshu the hirsute Hindustani heretic. Have no fear, I promise not to get blood on your waistcoat. *(He stuffs a sheet of rumpled newspaper into BILL's collar.)* There. One must be neat, you know.

(ADAMDONG and PASCAL ENTER. They are in a celebratory mood. A jaunty PASCAL is puffing away at his stogie, checking a long strand of ticker tape, tennis racquet under his arm.)

PASCAL. Just as I predicted, okra stock is beginning to bubble.

(When BILL spots PASCAL his eyes grow ever larger. He strains and struggles against his bounds; his muffled cries of anguish filter through the handkerchief.)

ADAMDONG. Ah, congratulations, Doctor, finally a patient after all these years.
PASCAL. Marvelous!

(The DOCTOR hands out business cards to ADAMDONG and PASCAL.)

DOCTOR. He was waiting for me upon my return. My card.
ADAMDONG. A banner day, indeed. First the International Research Scientists, now a patient. This calls for a toddy.

(He goes to the bar.)

PASCAL. I'll have a martini with a hickory nut, please.
DOCTOR. I'm torn between the alternatives of extraction.

(BILL kicks and strains, mumbles and groans throughout this segment in response to conversation and actions.)

ADAMDONG. *(Preparing drinks.)* How so?

DOCTOR. I'm undecided whether to go directly into the mouth or enter through an incision in the abdominal wall.

PASCAL. Oh, the latter method, of course. The standard procedure poses no challenge.

DOCTOR. I'd better sterilize.

(The DOCTOR goes to the refrigerator, removes a can of beer, opens it, pours the beer into his hands and washes them in it. He dries his hands roughly on his smock.)

ADAMDONG. A true medical visionary always attempts the impossible. Where would medicine be today without investigation?

PASCAL. Examination.

DOCTOR. Masturbation!

ADAMDONG. *(Coming with drinks.)* Medicine is always on the advance. Last year a basic office call—eighty dollars. This year—one hundred.

(ADAMDONG hands a drink to PASCAL and the DOCTOR. The men gather around the struggling, muted BILL.)

PASCAL. Perhaps the patient would like a drink.

DOCTOR. Yes. Drink, sir?

(BILL struggles and sputters.)

PASCAL. Apparently not.

ADAMDONG. Must be a teetotaler.

DOCTOR. Most commendable. I make it a practice of never having more than two drinks before surgery.

ADAMDONG. You say your patient was waiting for you upon your return?

DOCTOR. Yes.

ADAMDONG. Then he must have been alone with Ophelia. *(He speaks into Bill's ear.)* Sir, while you were private with Miss Rass did you perceive any... *(Hand from side to side.)* inconsistencies?

(BILL kicks and gurgles wildly.)

PASCAL. No doubt a man of utmost discretion.

DOCTOR. Your suspicions have become obsessive.

PASCAL. Jealousy is a destructive emotion, overrides the primary issues.

DOCTOR. Like bowling.

PASCAL. Precisely.

ADAMDONG. But there have been too many instances. One day I arrived home unexpectedly and discovered a short military man, clad only in socks, crouching in Ophelia's closet.

DOCTOR & PASCAL. Ahhhhhhhhhhhh.

ADAMDONG. I discerned he was a member of the armed services due to the fact his socks were khaki. So, thinking nimbly, I threw the man a quick salute and when he reacted instinctively by returning my salutation, he exposed a most imposing looking weapon of generous proportions.

DOCTOR & PASCAL. Ahhhhhhhhhhhh.

ADAMDONG. I interrogated the man mercilessly and he assured me that he was merely seeking refuge during maneuvers and that the item dangling from his lower extremities was nothing more than a well-disguised transmitting device.

PASCAL. A most legitimate explanation.

DOCTOR. You have nothing to fear. Ophelia is your loyal servant.

ADAMDONG. Perhaps.

DOCTOR. Without question.

PASCAL. What question?

DOCTOR. The question of collateral relative to the pigmies of the Paraguayan Peninsula.

PASCAL. *(Observing Bill.)* Doctor, your patient radiates a definite professional demeanor.

ADAMDONG. Yes. I wonder what his game is?

PASCAL. Mine is in the low eighties.

ADAMDONG. Really?

DOCTOR. *(Handing Pascal a card.)* My card.

PASCAL. Thank you.

ADAMDONG. The attaché case would indicate that he is a man of business persuasion.

PASCAL. Perhaps the contents of his case will give us a clue to his identity.

(As PASCAL lifts the case from the floor, BILL goes bananas under his restraints. PASCAL opens the case.)

ADAMDONG. Good thinking.

DOCTOR. Maybe he has knowledge of franchising.

(PASCAL rifles through the case as BILL goes silently mad.)

PASCAL. *(Throwing papers right and left into the air.)* A prodigious passel of profound papers.

ADAMDONG. He could be a reviewer.

DOCTOR. I do hope he gives me good notices. If so, I can take my extractions to Broadway.

ADAMDONG. It would be a great musical.

PASCAL. *(Concentrating on a paper. He reads:)* "Married filing joint return. Married filing separately. Unmarried head of household."

ADAMDONG. A marriage counselor!

DOCTOR. They do wonderful work.

ADAMDONG. And are grossly underpaid.

DOCTOR. I'll give him my special discount and he can keep his gums.

DOCTOR. *(Pulling a large, rusty wood saw from the pile of junk.)* I must proceed at once with the extraction.

(BILL struggles, and moans through the handkerchief.)

ADAMDONG. The poor devil appears to suffering inordinate pain.

(ADAMDONG and the PASCAL lean in close as the DOCTOR lowers the saw.)

DOCTOR. Now, say ah.

BILL. *(A muffled, but discernable cry for help.)* Halllllllp!

(He struggles against his bounds.)

PASCAL. A model patient.

(The men are distracted by the entrance of OPHELIA and CALVIN. OPHELIA, drink in hand, CALVIN, bouncy.)

OPHELIA. Ah! I see you've met Mr. Koontz of the IRS.

*(The men do a take at BILL squirming and groaning in the dental
    chair.)*

ADAMDONG, DOCTOR, PASCAL. IRS!
DOCTOR. *(Slamming the saw to the floor with disgust.)* Drat!
OPHELIA. Have we missed the presentation?
ADAMDONG. Most certainly not. We wouldn't dream of pro-
ceeding without you.
OPHELIA. Neeto!
CALVIN. Keeno!
OPHELIA. *(Lofts her glass as a toast.)* Drinko! *(She belts drink.)*
ADAMDONG. Doctor, please remove the fullness of floss.
DOCTOR. *(Unwinding the twine from BILL.)* He had all the
earmarks of a patient, too. An incrustation of the teeth consisting of
salivary secretion, food residue, and various salts.
ADAMDONG. Plus wing-tip shoes.

(The DOCTOR continues to unwind.)

OPHELIA. And honest mistake.
PASCAL. To err is human.
DOCTOR. *(Unwinding.)* Thank you.
PASCAL. *(Handing the DOCTOR the Doctor's card.)* Your card.

*(The DOCTOR takes the card and completes the unwinding. BILL,
    obviously near derangement, leaps from the chair and flees
    screaming from the room. The rest exchange looks of bewilder-
    ment and then face the audience and shrug their shoulders.
    CALVIN bounds forward and launches into a cheer, evoking
    audience participation.)*

CALVIN. Gimme an E—
EVERYONE. E!
CALVIN. Gimme an N—
EVERYONE. N!
CALVIN. Gimme a D—
EVERYONE. D!
CAST. T-H-E E-N-D!

(CALVIN turns to the DOCTOR and hands him a card.)

CALVIN. My card.

CURTAIN

TO LIVE AT THE PITCH

PROP LIST

Ball of yarn
Knitting needles
Stuffed squirrel
Mailman's pouch
Half-gallon of milk
Dirty drinking glass
Sandwich
Mailman's cap
Envelopes with letters
Calling cards
Chalk
Red, white, and blue megaphone with letters SHIT
Large ball of sturdy twine
Attaché case
Show shine equipment
Dental mirror
Camera
Two, one-dollar bills
Pocket watch
Old dental equipment
Saw, screw driver, hammer, hatchet, files, hand drill, pliers, etc.
Molar tooth
Set of negatives and photos
Bottle of gin

TO LIVE AT THE PITCH

Ticker tape
Pint of gin
Cigar
Golf club
Wall Street Journal
Large pocket watch with fob
Martini glasses
Simulated pumpkin
Lapel pin
Note pad
Pen
Handkerchief
Can of beer
Official looking papers
Rumpled newspapers
Wrist-watch

Hilarious Volumes of Short Comedies

What If?

Six Short Comedies from Jay D. Hanagan

(#25213)

Extra Curricular Activity
Fancy Meeting You Here
Last Laugh
She With A Capital Ess
Ships
Young Love

Senior Moments

Six Comedies for Older Actors

By Frederick Stroppel

(#20882)

After the Ball
Glacier Bay
Louie's Daughter
Sneeze
A World of Pleasure

The Argument/The Airport Play/
The Wedding Party

(#3166)

Three Comic Dramas from
Alexandra Gersten-Vassilaros

The Clean House
By Sarah Ruhl
2005 Pulitzer Prize Finalist

This extraordinary new play by an exciting new voice in the American drama was runner-up for the Pulitzer Prize. The play takes place in what the author describes as "metaphysical Connecticut", mostly in the home of a married couple who are both doctors. They have hired a housekeeper named Matilde, an aspiring comedian from Brazil who's more interested in coming up with the perfect joke than in house-cleaning. Lane, the lady of the house, has an eccentric sister named Virginia who's just nuts about house-cleaning. She and Matilde become fast friends, and Virginia takes over the cleaning while Matilde works on her jokes. Trouble comes when Lane's husband Charles reveals that he has found his soul mate, or "bashert" in a cancer patient named Anna, on whom he has operated. The actors who play Charles and Anna also play Matilde's parents in a series of dream-like memories, as we learn the story about how they literally killed each other with laughter, giving new meaning to the phrase, "I almost died laughing." This theatrical and wildly funny play is a whimsical and poignant look at class, comedy and the true nature of love. 1m, 4f (#6266)

"Fresh, funny ... a memorable play, imbued with a somehow comforting philosophy: that the messes and disappointments of life are as much a part of its beauty as romantic love and chocolate ice cream, and a perfect punch line can be as sublime as the most wrenchingly lovely aria." — *NY Times*